Contents

RIP
Really Implausible People

Here lie
The ashes
Of Jim 'Houseproud'
Groover
Who sucked himself up
With a powerful Hoover

Here lie
The remains
Of 'Fast' Eddy Jakes
Who invented a sports car
Without any brakes

Here lies
The body
Of Annabel Smedley
Who took an eternity pill
Which proved deadly

Here lies
The top half
of 'Dithering' Freddy
The rest will come soon
When it feels
That it's ready

Lindsay Macrae

Skateboard Skatedown

I'm zipping
and I'm flying
and I'm popping off the curb
I am greased lightning down a hillside
gaining airspeed like a bird

My hair's slicked back by the air-flow
my t-shirt's flapping in the breeze
I'm a speedy skateboard rider
I'm a rider on the breeze

I wear air-conditioned blue-jeans
so my knees poke through the holes
shoelaces fly out from my runners
quicksilver fuels my toes

I need kneepads for this madness
and a bike crash helmet, too
I'm a breathless skateboard rider
look out world, I'm flying through!

Maxine Tyne

Everything is Rhythmical

Rhythm rhythm
Can you
Hear the
Rhythm

Quick rhythm
slick rhythm
God given
Life livin

Rhythm rhythm
Can you
Hear the
rhythm

If you listen close
Ears to the ground
The bass of noise
Is rhythm's sound
From spoken word
To ways of walk
From rap to reggae
And funk we talk (in)

Rhythm rhythm
Can you
Hear the
Rhythm

Way back in the heart of Africa
They took our drums away
But rhythm proved its own power
By being here today

All four corners sweet-sounding
    rhythms reach
With treble in the speaker, even bass
    in speech
From the freezing cold to heat in heights
Mohammed Ali did use it in his fights

With

Quick rhythm
Slick rhythm
Gold rhythm
Bold rhythm
God given
Life livin

Rhythm rhythm
Can you
Hear the
Rhythm

Lemn Sissay

Newsflash

There has been a disaster
At the Magic Show.

Rosalie was cut in half
And looks likely to remain so.

We understand that the magician responsible
Is not available for comment,
As he seems to have vanished
Along with his doves, magic wand
And sixteen coloured handkerchiefs.

A white rabbit, however,
Is being held for questioning.

Rosalie is said to be
Putting a brave face on it
Which is not easy
When she hasn't a leg to stand on.

If anyone can supply
Human super-glue
Invisible sticky-tape
Or the whereabouts of the missing magician,
The police, not to mention Rosalie,
Will be delighted to hear from them.

June Crebbin

5

A LIMERICK

there once was a limerick called Steven
whose rhyme scheme was very uneven
it didn't make sense
it wasn't funny
and who'd call a limerick Steven anyway?

ANOTHER LIMERICK

there once was a limerick about Mr Jones

but Mr Jones found it and

ripped

it

up.

Steven Herrick

ACROSTIC

A poem teachers make all the
Class write because
Rhyming poems are too hard
On our brains
So anybody, even a Maths
Teacher could write
In the
aCrostic style!

by Mr Sharp (Year 5 Maths Teacher)

Spare a Thought

Spare a thought for the front-door mat,
Scratching-pad of a mangy cat,
Mud-gunged, balding, full of holes,
Poked by high-heels, scraped by soles,
Worn, downtrodden, booted flat –
Spare a thought for the front-door mat.

Spare a thought for the hoover, please,
Gobbling grit and mongrel fleas,
Kicked by chair-legs, bruised by doors,
Choked by dust and fluffy floors –
No surprise its innards wheeze –
Spare a thought for the hoover, please.

Spare a thought for the bathroom soap,
Clawed and gouged by clumsy grope,
Rubbed round armpits, dirty faces,
Feet and other nasty places,
Life for soap's a slippery slope –
Spare a thought for the bathroom soap.

Spare a thought for all punished things –
Trampolines and wrestling rings,
Nails being hammered, gongs being bashed,
Eggs being beaten, spuds being mashed,
Dartboards, drums and sofa springs,
Oh, spare a thought for punished things!

Richard Edwards

Can We Have Our Ball Back, Please?

England gave football to the world
Who, now they've got the knack
Play it better than we do
And won't let us have it back.

Gareth Owen

Western Civilization

Sheets of tin nailed to posts
driven in the ground
make up the house.

Some rags complete
the intimate landscape.

The sun slanting through cracks
welcomes the owner

After twelve hours of slave
labour.
breaking rock
shifting rock
breaking rock
shifting rock
fair weather
wet weather
breaking rock
shifting rock

Old age comes early.

A mat on dark nights
is enough when he dies
gratefully
of hunger.

Agostinho Neto

translated by *Margaret Dickinson*

RULES

Governments rule most countries,
Bankers rule most banks,
Captains rule their football teams
And piranhas rule fish tanks.

There are rules for gnobling gnomes
And rules for frying frogs,
There are rules for biting bullies
And for vexing vicious dogs.

There are rules for driving motor cars
And crashing into chums,
There are rules for taking off your pants
And showing spotty bums.

There are rules for nasty children
Who tie bangers to old cats,
There are rules for running riot
And rules for burning bats.

NO EATING IN THE CLASSROOM

PANTS TO BE REMOVED ON THURSDAYS ONLY

PLEASE FRY YOUR FROGS BETWEEN 6 A.M. AND 8 P.M.

WAIT

Do Not WALK ON THE GRASS

WALK

DON'T WALK

There are rules in the classroom.
There are rules in the street.
Some rules are wild and woolly
And some are tame and neat.

And some are pretty sensible
And some are pretty daft;
Some I take quite seriously,
At others I have laughed.

But there is one special rule
You should not be without:
If you do not like the rules
OPEN YOUR MOUTH AND SHOUT!
OPEN YOUR MOUTH AND SHOUT!

Brian Patten

Lord Neptune

Build me a castle,
the young boy cried,
as he tapped his father's knee.
But make it tall
and make it wide,
with a king's throne just for me.

An echo drifted on the wind,
sang deep and wild and free:
Oh you can be king of the castle,
but I am lord of the sea.

Give me your spade,
the father cried;
let's see what we can do!
We'll make it wide
so it holds the tide,
with a fine throne just for you.

He dug deep down
in the firm damp sand,
for the tide was falling fast.
The moat was deep,
the ramparts high,
and the turrets tall and vast.

Now I am king,
the young boy cried,
and this is my golden throne!
I rule the sands,
I rule the seas;
I'm lord of all lands, alone!

The sand-king ruled
from his golden court
and it seemed the wind had died;
but at dusk his throne
sank gently down
in Neptune's rolling tide.

And an echo rose upon the wind,
sang deep and wild and free:
Oh you may be king of the castle,
but I am lord of the sea.

Judith Nicholls

12

I'd Like to Squeeze

I'd like to squeeze this round world
into a new shape

I'd like to squeeze this round world
like a tube of toothpaste

I'd like to squeeze this world
fair and square

I'd like to squeeze it and squeeze it
till everybody had an equal share

John Agard

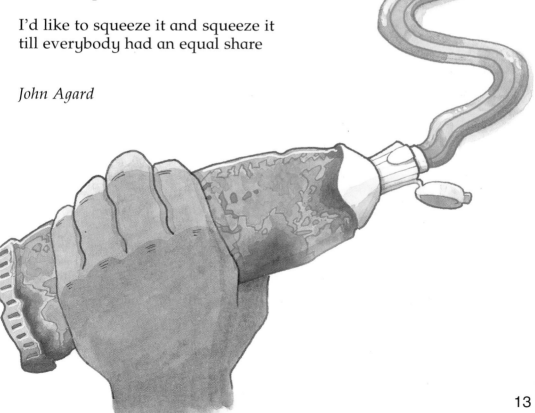

OUR TEACHER

Our teacher taps his toes,
keeping the beat to some silent tune
only he knows.

Our teacher drums his fingers
on his desk, on the window,
on anything, when the room is quiet,
when we're meant to be writing
in silence.

Our teacher cracks his knuckles,
clicks his fingers, grinds his teeth,
his knees are knocking the edge of his desk,
he breathes to a rhythmical beat.

When he turns his head in a certain way
there's a bone that cracks in his neck.
When he sinks to the floor
we often think he'll stay on his knees
for ever more, he's such a physical wreck!

Our teacher bangs his head against the wall
(or pretends to) when someone comes up
with another dumb remark.

Our teacher says we annoy him
with all our silly fuss.
Perhaps he's never really thought
how much he irritates us.

Brian Moses

Guess

My first is in rattle but not in creak
My second's in creak but not in squeak
My third is in squeak and also in squeal
my fourth is in whistle and also in shrill
my fifth is in clanking and clanging and iron
my whole is the monster who roars on the line.

Berlie Doherty

Answer: I am a train.

the clowns are not really happy

the clowns are not really happy
the clowns are not really sad
they just make mistakes
like me and you
maybe they didn't mean to be clowns
it was all just a big mistake

it's their mistakes that make us laugh
mistakes don't really make us happy
mistakes don't really make us sad
we laugh because we know
we make the same mistakes too

we're laughing at our own mistakes
we're laughing while we sit and watch
someone else making our mistakes instead

we're laughing because we dream in bed
one night we'll make the same mistake
and wake up in the morning to find
we've all turned into clowns

Dave Ward

Blue Hair

In between the dinner ladies
runs the blue-haired boy,
spilling beans and jelly,
and all us kids are yelling
"Catch him! Catch Blue Hair!"
though mostly we like him,
would like to be like him
but wouldn't dare. And look,
he's out front again –
the forks are clattering down –
and haring past our tables,
our laughing, screaming tables,
with five teachers in pursuit
(they'll never catch Blue Hair!).
And none of us can eat,
we're banging with our spoons,
blowing with our breaths,
erupting in a roar
as Blue Hair dodges everyone
and bursts out the door.

Matthew Sweeney

MISS MUFFETT

Dear Miss Muffett,

Are your picnics spoilt by
– buzzings in your ear
– swoopings in your face
– fallings in your curds-and-whey?
In short: are you troubled by
  F L I E S ?
Ours is a GREEN company.
We use only ecologically sound
Recycled webs.
Our representative
is close to you NOW
and looks forward to
sitting down with you
to discuss your needs.

The Rent-A-Spider Company plc

Michael Harrison

Rainforest

After a boat trip down the Franklin River in Tasmania

Oh don't bring down
the ancient pine,
the breath of life
that's yours and mine.

Don't tear it out
saw it down
gouge it, chop it,
let it drown.

Don't fell the tree
that's stood so long,
Leave bird and bush
where they belong.

Leave the forest,
green gold place,
the glow of hope
on this earth's
old face.

Libby Hathorn

19

Jam – A Prophecy

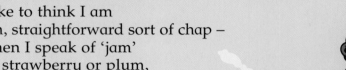

> *This is the way the world ends*
> *Not with a bang but a whimper.*
>
> T S Eliot

I'll try to make it clear at once –
    I like to think I am
A plain, straightforward sort of chap –
    When I speak of 'jam'
It isn't strawberry or plum,
    Or apricot, or fruit
Of any kind at all: I speak
    About the *traffic* jam;
Not your usual simple chain
    Of vans and juggernauts,
Old bangers, coupés, limousines,
    Saloons and nippy sports,
Stretching down the motorway,
    Along the country lanes,
Or city streets or avenues:
    No, I foresee a day
When every inch of space is filled,
    And there is just no way
That any vehicle can move,
    And that is how they'll stay.
And, what is more, I'm speaking of
    Not only the UK,
But all the traffic of the world,
    Static, nose to tail,
All hooting on their horns like mad,
    And all to no avail.

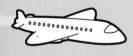

Then gradually the noise will fade
    And slowly die away
As batteries give up the ghost
    And darkness follows day.
And if you think the skies provide
    Some prospect of escape
I sadly fear that you will make
    A very grave mistake,
For overhead the skies are jammed
    With planes of every kind,
Wing to wing and nose to tail,
    And, looking up, you'll find,
Just one enormous metal sheet,
    Huge jigsaw made of steel,
Covering the clouds and stars;
    And so I can reveal
The awful truth: the world will end
    Not with a bang or wham,
Not with a whimper, not with
    a slam,
    But a global traffic jam.

Vernon Scannell

21

The Man in Brown

Grandma's got a photo of a man in brown.
She said he went to war.
I said I'd like to be a soldier too
But Grandma said, "What for?"
I said I'd like to be a hero too,
And shoot all the baddies down.
"And kill someone's brother?" asked Grandma,
"Like they killed the man in brown?"
There's nothing to be gained by fighting,
There's plenty to lose, I'm sure.
It takes a coward to start a fight,
A hero to stop a war.

Jeanne Willis

The Barber

His pole with pewter basins hung,
Black rotten teeth in order strung,
Rang'd cups, that in the window stood,
Lin'd with red rags to look like blood,
Did well his threefold trade explain,
Who shav'd, drew teeth, and breath'd a vein.

Anon

HAIRCUTS
2d

23

Speak Gently

I

Speak gently to the little child!
    Its love be sure to gain;
Teach it in accents soft and mild—
    It may not long remain.

Speak gently to the young: for they
    Will have enough to bear;
Pass through this life as best they may,
    Tis full of anxious care!

David Bates

II

Speak roughly to your little boy,
    And beat him when he sneezes:
He only does it to annoy,
    Because he knows it teases.

I speak severely to my boy,
    I beat him when he sneezes;
For he can thoroughly enjoy
    The pepper when he pleases!

Lewis Carroll

Twinkle, Twinkle, Little Star

TWINKLE, twinkle, little star!
I don't wonder what you are.
Teacher told us yesterday
Why you come and go away;
And she let us have a wrinkle
Why you seem to twinkle, twinkle;
You are just a whirling mass
Of different sorts of burning gas,
Rushing through the places where
There really isn't even air;
Rushing on at miles a second
(Teacher told us how it's reckoned).
And she told us yesterday
You're so many leagues away
That, if some great water-spout
Were to burst and put you out,
None would know your light had fled
Until long after we were dead
So you may twinkle, little star,
But *I* don't wonder what you are.

A M P Dawson

Rising Sun

Softly, softly, Lisa-O!
Softly, O Sun-God!
Do not ravish the world.
Ram pawing the earth with hooves of flame,
Ram pounding the earth with horns of fire,
Do not ravish the world,
Do not destroy us!

Fon

SINGING SAND

We are the dunes of singing sand
singing
singing
songs sung low
songs of caravans
songs of camel bells
We are the dunes of singing sand
singing
singing
silken songs
songs of quartz on wings of wind
singing
singing
our desert song.

Sonja Dunn

POSTCARD

Soaking up the sun in Woking.
Only joking.
Really soaking.
Tent is leaking.
Never spend a week in Woking!

Duncan Forbes

Asleep

A child said,
"There are people in our graveyard
who are not dead.
They are not dead at all,
but they are in graves."

Ghosts?
Spooks?
Spectres?

I went to see for myself,
and there it was,
as plain as a pig!
The words were carved on the stone;
"In loving memory of Ethel,
Who fell asleep on the 13th May 1910."
I listened for sounds of snoring,
but all was silent.
Plainly, Ethel was a quiet sleeper,
but what an odd place for a sleep!
And surely it must be true?
Who would carve a lie so deeply in stone?
I listened again,
but all was silent.
What about the church-bells?
Wouldn't they waken her?
Then what?
Then what?

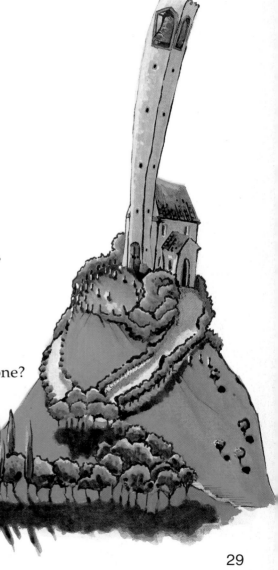

John Cunliffe

A Dyer of Cloth
(St Nicholas' Church, Yarmouth)

Here lies a man who first did dye,
When he was twenty-four,
And yet he lived to reach the age
Of hoary hairs, fourscore.
But now he's gone, and certain 'tis
He'll not dye any more.

Anon

WALNUT

MULBERRY

MADDER

DYER'S GREENWEED

WOAD

DYER'S BUGLOSS

Don't

Don't comb your hair in company.
Don't cross the kitchen floor in welly boots.
Don't put the television on.
Don't squint. Don't get in fights.

Don't stuff your mouth with sausage.
Don't drop towels on the bathroom floor.
Don't hang about with that rough crowd.
Don't put your feet up on the chair.

Don't use up all the paper in the loo.
Don't scratch. Don't twitch. Don't sniff. Don't talk.
Don't stick your tongue out.
Don't you dare to answer back.

Life is full of opportunity, says my Mum.

Barrie Wade

31

Index of poem features